A SECOND DORSET QUIZ BOOK

To test your knowled
places, custc
characters of t

The cottages form part of a dairy complex known as
The Ring. In which village?

Jean Bellamy

Illustrations by Helen Fenton

J.B. Publications

By the same author
A Dorset Quiz Book 1995
Other publications
Cornish Mystery (Marshall Pickering 1986)
The Haunted Island (Marshall Pickering 1990)
Treasures of Dorset (Thornhill Press 1991)
Tomb of the Black Gull (Kevin Mayhew 1997)

First published in 1997 by S. B. Publications,
c/o 19 Grove Road, Seaford, East Sussex BN25 1TP

©1997 Jean Bellamy

ISBN 1 85770 135 6

Designed and typeset by CGB, Lewes
Printed by MFP Design and Print
Longford Trading Estate, Thomas Street,
Stretford, Manchester M32 0JT

CONTENTS

Front cover: Where and what is this object and by whom was it set up?
Back cover: The oldest working post-box in England. W^l ʒ it?

INTRODUCTION

HERE is another quiz book to test your knowledge of Dorset. As before, the questions range from the easy and moderately easy to the quite difficult - as has been pointed out to me. Hopefully, however, there is something in it for everyone and, as before, the answers can all be found by turning to the back part of the book.

Single word answers can be somewhat unsatisfactory, so again I have included additional information to provide further interest.

There is no grading system, and no penalties for not knowing the answers - unless you wish to institute your own scoring system. It is a book to be taken up or put down at any time and the questions may be taken in any order.

Jean Bellamy
Upwey
Weymouth

1 DORSET BOOK OF RECORDS

Above the noise and stir of
yonder fields
Uplifted on this height I feel
the mind
Expand itself in wider liberty.
From *Lewesdon Hill*
by the Reverend William Crowe

1 What is the second highest point in Dorset?

2 Where is the oldest fire engine in Dorset to be seen?

3 Where is the only silk-spinning machine of its kind in Dorset – and in the whole of England?

4 This parish church is the largest in Dorset.

5 Which is Dorset's most northerly village?

6 In its conformation, this vast breakwater is unique in Dorset and in the world.

7 Where is the oldest pillar box still in use in Britain?

8 It is the second largest natural harbour in the world.

9 This village, on the slopes of Bulbarrow, has a six-acre picnic place, which was the first of its kind in the county.

10 This tract of Dorset forest is said to be one of the few remaining primeval woodlands in England.

2 FAMOUS MEN

Be of good comfort, O my children
For ye shall be remembered
Inscription on a memorial at
Bradford Abbas

1 This man is a popular tourist attraction.

2 Who was Jack Ketch?

3 There is a large effigy of this British soldier, archeologist and author in St Martins-on-the-Wall, Wareham. Who is he?

4 Two members of a family immortalised by Thomas Hardy lie buried in Piddletrenthide church. Who are they?

5 In which museum is there a portrait, presumed to be of Admiral Sir Thomas Masterman Hardy, to be found?

6 Name the Elizabethan adventurer and explorer, born in Lyme Regis, who discovered the Bermuda Islands.

7 A British Army general and defender of Mafeking had connections with a Dorset island. Who was he and what island?

8 The family home of this BBC announcer and famous wartime news reader was at Broadstone, a suburb of Poole. Who was he?

9 In 1893, a great British statesman nearly lost his life as a child while climbing a bridge. Who was he and where did the event occur?

10 Two famous Dorset men who had similar names, had a common ancestor who died in 1599. There is a memorial tablet to him in St Peter's Church, Dorchester. Who were the men and what was the name of their ancestor?

3 THE ARTS

Happy life's duties with its joys to blend
Reynolds his master, Henderson his friend.
Epitaph to Dorset portrait painter, Thomas Beach,
born at Milton Abbas in 1738.

1 Where is there a watercolour of *The Schoolhouse at Mere* by William Barnes?

2 This theatre manager, born in 1765 in Nottinghamshire, opened a theatre in Bridport in 1826.

3 She lived at Fontmell Magna, and was skilled in the art of dressing dolls and creating needlework pictures from her drawings. She died in 1976.

4 This prolific artist was born in 1772 in Honiton, and later lived in Weymouth. Many of his watercolours, pen-and-wash pictures, and engravings feature scenes from the Dorset landscape.

5 One of the most famous of English landscape and marine artists painted scenes of Weymouth Bay in the early nineteenth century. Who was he?

6 This architect, sculptor and painter was born at Blandford in 1817. At the age of sixteen he went to Italy to study engraving.

7 In the old church at Kingston is a medallion of John Scott, first Earl of Eldon and a former Lord Chancellor of England. It is by a sculptor who left a fortune to the Royal Academy when he died in 1842. Who was he?

8 This Dorset musician, instrumentalist, and composer was a conductor of choirs for thirty years or more at the turn of the century.

9 In June 1793, a theatre was opened at Blandford to replace the old building previously used. What was it called and who opened it?

10 Who was the Weymouth bookseller and publisher who lived from 1752-1793, and did much to promote interest in local art. He studied at the Royal Academy, and was notable for his portly proportions.

7

4 CASTLES

Guardian of Fate,
By Corvie's gate,
A soaring castle springs.

Dr Bevan Whitney of
Ower Quay, Poole Harbour

1 Name the part Norman, part Tudor castle in the South Dorset heathland that today takes guests.

2 There were a number of motte and bailey castles in Dorset, although most of the baileys have disappeared. Several mottes remain, the two most easily accessible being at Christchurch – and which other town?

3 This castle, situated in 640 acres of parkland, is built of stone taken from a nearby abbey.

4 Name the castle, now a ruin, which stands on the edge of a cliff overlooking a harbour.

5 Who built Sherborne's new castle as a high block with four towers and many chimneys. Thirty years later four wings were added and four more towers. By whom?

6 Sir John Arundell lived in this splendid sixteenth century castle which once existed near the church of this small south-west Dorset town.

7 What is the name of the castle built by James Wyatt for John Penn in 1800, and named after an ancestor of his. And where is it situated?

8 Henry VIII built this castle to protect an anchorage.

9 The remains of this small ancient British castle standing near a railway line are alternatively known as Spetisbury Rings.

10 Where is the fake castle built by George Burt (1816–1894) and the Weymouth architect, G R Crickmay?

5 SOME NOTABLE WOMEN

At length with age-worn steps and slow
but never weary love
She went who is our Mother still,
though now she rests above.
The Reverend Handley C G Moule

1 What was Florence Nightingale's connection with Westbourne, Bournemouth?

2 The alabaster tomb of her parents may be seen in this Minster church, and she founded a grammar school nearby.

3 Horton Church is said to be the only one in England named after this saint.

4 This fictional character was a Dorset dairymaid.

5 No one knows the identity of the Lady Bountiful who is buried in a hamlet in the Blackmoor Vale, three miles from Sturminster Newton. By what name was she known?

6 She bought an island in 1927 with the intention of keeping it as a nature reserve, free from human interference.

7 This woman fell into the sea in 1896 and only her stump remains.

8 She was one of the founders of the Dorset Trust for Nature Conservancy and set up the Portland Bird Observatory.

9 This clergyman's wife had six sons, one of whom was a friend of Thomas Hardy.

10 She was a resident of Sandbanks, Poole, and one of the first women to hold a racehorse trainer's licence She was still working at over ninety years of age.

6 DORSET DIALECT

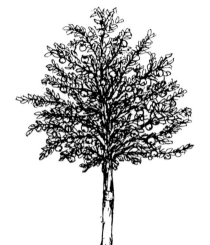

An there vor me the apple tree
Do lean down low in Linden Lee
William Barnes, 1800–1886.

1 What is a chicken doing if it is 'spuddling'?

2 What sort of creatures are cullywigs?

3 If you said, 'He cassen zee as well as cou's c'as', what would you be saying?

4 What sort of animal is a sh-'ow-crop?

5 If someone said, 'Mid rain 's know you', what would they be telling you?

6 What would you be meaning if you said, 'It do want a drillen'?

7 If someone's car is a-stooded, what has happened to it?

8 If you were gathering gilcups in a field, what would you be picking?

9 If you called someone a lummick, what would you be calling him?

10 What time of day is s'atternoon?

7 MEN OF THE CLOTH

His name was 'Dear and venerable'
among his beloved people.
(See Question 4)

1 A folly was erected by this clergyman in 1817. Who was he, and where was the hill on which he built it?

2 He was one of three bishops to be born in Blandford. He became Archbishop of Canterbury.

3 He was Bishop of London from 1901 to 1939 and he played golf at Broadstone, a suburb of Poole.

4 He was the vicar of Fordington St George, Dorchester, for fifty-one years.

5 This bishop, who befriended Richard II and challenged Bolingbroke, became the vicar of Sturminster Marshall towards the end of his life.

6 In 1713, Dr Charles Sloper built the church of which he was rector, at his own expense. Which church?

7 He was the ancestor of two Prime Ministers and a rector of Blandford St Mary from 1645-72. Who was he?

8 Richard Poore, Bishop of Salisbury and builder of the cathedral there, was baptised in this church in 1217.

9 This son of a vicar of Winterborne Whitchurch tried to make a little money by farming but lost it and was imprisonerd for debt in Lincoln Castle.

10 A volume of sermons by this seventeenth century vicar of a Dorset parish are in the chained library in Wimborne Minster. Name him.

8 MISCELLANEOUS

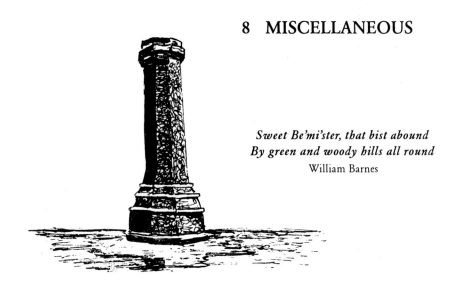

*Sweet Be'mi'ster, that bist abound
By green and woody hills all round*
William Barnes

1 It was built in 1790 and it is the highest of the county's follies and visible from most of East Dorset.

2 In 1884 he excavated the four acre site of a Romano-British village at Woodcutts.

3 Where will you find the Orrery Clock?

4 Where will you find a pair of leg irons once used by prisoners walking between Poole and Dorchester?

5 '. . . its piers, its groves of pines, its promenades, its covered gardens. . .' To which town is Thomas Hardy referring?

6 Where is the Shell Grotto?

7 *Erica Ciliaris*, otherwise known as Dorset Heath, grows only here.

8 On the top of Golden Cap, a memorial is to be found. Who does it commemorate?

9 Thomas Hardy called this town 'Emminster'.

10 This town had – and still has – its stocks, whipping post and a ducking stool.

9 INDUSTRY

*Industry is the soul of busy-
ness and the keystone of
prosperity.*
Charles Dickens

1 Where can you see demonstrations of silk-spinning?

2 How did Inigo Jones bring new life and prosperity to Portland?

3 Who tried unsuccessfully to start a china clay industry on an island?

4 Which town once made ropes for hangmen?

5 Who were the architect builders who rebuilt Blandford after a fire ?

6 There is a gloving factory at this North Dorset town.

7 A motor car called the Gush Special, later renamed the Vitesce, was
   produced in this town in the early Thirties. The company went
   bankrupt in 1934.

8 Swanage was the birthplace of this stone-quarry boy who, at the
   beginning of the 1800s, went to London and founded the great
   international contractors' firm that bears his name.

9 Where is Dorset's largest vineyard?

10 There was a flourishing cloth trade in this North Dorset town around
    1450.

10 A QUESTION OF SPORT

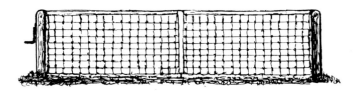

It is a poor sport that is not worth the candle.
George Herbert

1 Where is there a Viking Windsurfing School?

2 In 1806, Squire Farquharson purchased what remained of Eastbury House at Tarrant Gunville. To what use did he put it?

3 What traditional event takes place on Boxing Day at Portesham?

4 This unusual sport is also connected with Portesham, where it is said to have originated. Two large teams armed with dustbin lids and spoons on sticks chase a block of wood along footpaths. What is it called?

5 This Elizabethan poet wrote, *inter alia*, books on falconry and hunting. He was born at Winterborne Whitchurch.

6 Nets used at the Wimbledon Tennis Championships are made here.

7 He was an MP and a Ranger of Cranborne Chase and belonged to a family obsessed by hunting. Who was he?

8 Point-to-point meetings are held here in spring and autumn – on Easter Monday and Boxing Day.

9 A gift connected with an ancient game was bequeathed by the village of Walditch to Bridport and West Dorset Sports Trust by Mr Joseph Gundry in recent times. What was it?

10 This sport – an old tradition connected with boats – involved rowing out into the bay at Weymouth.

11 CUSTOMS AND TRADITIONS

*Wood and straw do burn
likewise,
Take care the *blankers
don't dout your eyes*
See Question 7

* *flying objects*

1 An ancient fair, lasting five days and the largest in Dorset, was held here from the twelfth century until the beginning of the First World War.

2 What was Pack Monday Fair, and where did it take place?

3 What was the Byzant or Bezant?

4 What old custom takes place in Abbotsbury every year on 13 May?

5 Which age-old custom was revived in Poole during this century?

6 In 1268, Henry II granted a charter to Martinstown. For what purpose?

7 What curious old custom used to take place on Portland on Bonfire Night and which other custom connected with Portland was still practised until almost the middle of the last century?

8 What alarming looking creature used to appear at various assemblages held at this Dorset village during the Christmas holiday period?

9 It is said to be one of the oldest and most interesting of Purbeck customs and it took place at Wareham on the four evenings preceding the last Friday in November.

10 A more recent annual event now takes place every August, and is becoming one of Dorset's most celebrated. What is it?

12 TOWNS

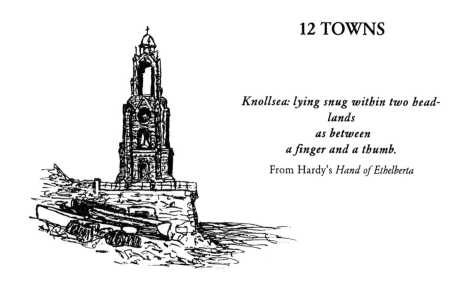

Knollsea: lying snug within two head-
lands
as between
a finger and a thumb.

From Hardy's *Hand of Ethelberta*

1 In which town did Giles Winterborne wait for Grace by a fourteenth century conduit, and which of Thomas Hardy's books records the incident?

2 Of this North Dorset town, Robert Louis Stevenson said that one would not be surprised to see 'a centurion coming up the street with a fatigue draft of legionaries'.

3 Which town did Hardy refer to as Shaston?

4 This seaside town contains many a discarded London relic, including the Wellington Clock Tower.

5 Which seaside town did Hardy call Knollsea?

6 A shopping arcade has been built on the site of a well known school in this town.

7 Orphaned as a result of a fire, many children of this town were given the town's name as a surname .

8 This town was called Leddenton in Hardy's *Jude the Obscure.*

9 In which Dorset town will you find the Russell Cotes Art Gallery and Museum?

10 The Saxon name of this town, originally in Hampshire, was Twinham.

13 VILLAGES

1 Its name means 'sheep village'. Which village is it?

2 Hardy wrote of this village as Owlscombe.

3 A Martyr Tree and a memorial shelter are to be found here.

4 There are variations of this village's name in the *Domesday Book*. It is recorded as Abristentona, as Ebrictinton and as Edbrichton. How is it known today?

5 In which village will you find God's Blessing Green and Pig Oak?

6 How did the oddly-named village of Hammoon come to be so named?

7 A brook runs through these three villages, and nearby is the old Roman road, Ackling Dyke.

8 Wild boar would seem to have roamed this hamlet on Cranborne Chase.

9 From his manor house in this village Thomas Chafin rode out to oppose the Duke of Monmouth when he landed at Lyme Regis.

10 Oliver Cromwell marched into this village with around 300 prisoners whom he locked in the church for the night.

14 FOLKLORE

We Dorset folk are not without our odd beliefs

Henry Moule, son of the
Reverend Henry Moule

1 Where is the Miraculous Beam to be found?

2 Where are the 'Music Barrows', and why are they so called?

3 What is the legend connected with St Augustine's Well at Cerne Abbas?

4 An animal was said to have been walled up in a priest's hole at Athelhampton. What was it?

5 At Little Mayne, near West Knighton, is an ancient stone circle What does local legend claim – inaccurately – it to be?

6 According to legend, no one has ever seen this Dorset river rise. Which river?

7 According to tradition, the foundations of this church in north-west Dorset were originally intended to be built in a nearby wood. During the night, however, what was built by day was moved to where the church now stands.

8 According to legend, the ghostly tolling of a bell underwater is supposed to be heard once a year by anyone standing on the bridge above. Where is the bridge?

9 According to legend, why did a ship carrying bells for St James Church, Poole, sink along the stretch of coast between Swanage and Ballard Down?

10 This chapel was built, according to legend, by a local squire who, after his daughter's wedding, saw both her and her bridegroom drown at sea.

15 DES RES

The bright-tunn'd house a-risen proud
Stood high avore a zummer cloud,
Upon the many-window'd wall.
An' windy sheades o' tow'rs did vall
William Barnes

1 Parts of this East Dorset venerable old manor house are said to date from the reign of the Saxon King Athelstan.

2 This early seventeenth century manor was Squire Derriman's Oxwell Hall in *The Trumpet Major.*

3 This mediaeval stately home is reputed to be the site of King Athelstan's palace.

4 Thomas Masterman Hardy of Trafalgar fame was born here in 1769.

5 This manor was held by the Harang or Herring family since the early fourteenth century and Christmas feasts held there are described in poems by William Barnes.

6 One of Dorset's oldest houses stands on the banks of the Stour. Its Saxon owner is named in the Domesday Book and one wing is called John of Gaunt's Kitchen.

7 'It befits me not, being a member of the house, to speak of it'. Who wrote those words and about which house?

8 This great Tudor house was owned for many generations by the famous Strangways family.

9 The garden of this mid-Dorset mediaeval manor house still retains its Tudor plan and contains a bowling green flanked by a great yew hedge, and a columbarium.

10 The central part of this house was built by Sir William Napier in the mid-1700s to replace an earlier house that had been burnt down.

16 PUBS

And the little brown nightingale
bills his best,
And they sit outside at The
Traveller's Rest '

Weathers, by Thomas Hardy

1 How did Hardy refer to the White Horse Inn at Middlemarsh?

2 Where will you find Hardy's Lornton Inn?

3 This pub on Portland was originally the Clerk's House. It became an inn during the reign of the king whose name it bears.

4 An original mahogany panel from the wreck of the cargo ship, *Lord Duffas,* which foundered in 1894 with the loss of all hands, is in the King's Shilling Bar of this inn.

5 Where is the World's End Inn?

6 Where will you find the Square and Compass?

7 This pub, situated on an island, became known by the name of the island's new owner.

8 In *Under the Greenwood Tree* Dick Dewy and Fanny stopped to have tea and rest the horse at this inn.

9 Which pub is the Pure Drop Inn of Hardy's *Tess of the D'Urbevilles?*

10 Where will you find an inn sign showing the True Lover's Knot?

17 MISCELLANEOUS

Zoo now I hope his kindly
feace
Is gone to vind a better pleace
But still wi' vo'k a left behind
He'll always be a'kept in mind
William Barnes

1 Where will you find the Tricycle Museum?

2 Where and what is Scaplen's Court?

3 From this hill, which sounds like a place to take a walk, you get a fine view of a harbour.

4 The church in this village about eight miles north of Dorchester shares its name with a well-known London station, as does the village.

5 William Barnes' poem printed above appears on a plinth. Where?

6 Which of Hardy's novels was published anonymously in 1872?

7 Where and what is Flowers Barrow?

8 What was the Reeve Pole?

9 It is said to be one of the finest stretches of Roman road in Britain.

10 Over the door to which cottage will you find the words 'why worry?' inscribed in Greek?

18 ROYALTY

Never was sorrow more sincere
Than that which flowed round Charlotte's bier.
Couplet found in an old schoolbook.

1 The bones of which English king were unearthed in Shaftesbury in January 1931?

2 This queen, as a child, slept in a hotel at Swanage.

3 Which town was King Canute's landing place?

4 Two brothers of a king were laid to rest in this abbey.

5 A king sent his daughter to this house in its 400 acre park, with orders that she should not be allowed to see her mother. Who was the king, who was his daughter, and which was the house?

6 In the 1960s, this elegant late eighteenth century house overlooking Poole Harbour was occupied by a prince. Who was he and which is the house?

7 Who was the eighth century king of Wessex and England who split the large diocese of Winchester into two and also founded an abbey.

8 Which monarch granted the first charter to Bridport?

9 Which event was Corfe Castle's market cross erected to celebrate?

10 Nash Court at Marnhull, now rebuilt, was the residence of this queen.

19 UNNATURAL DEATHS

We heard the drub of Dead Man's Bay
Where bones of thousands are.

Thomas Hardy. *The Dynasts.*

1 Who was found in a cliffside grave,
   beheaded and with her lower jaw
   removed. The discovery of coins put
   her death towards the end of the
   third century.

2 How did a member of the Mohun
   family of Fleet die in 1757?

3 How did Sam Hookey, the smuggler of Wick, Christchurch, meet his
   death?

4 Two members of the Harvey family are buried in the church of St Mary,
   Bradford Abbas. How did they die?

5 During the seventeenth century, the figure of this woman was seen by a
   judge during a dinner at a house in Charminster, with her throat cut
   and holding her head under her arm. Who was she?

6 The state of some skeletons found near a ruined fourteenth century
   church have led some archeologists to believe that they were the victims
   of human sacrifice. Where were they found?

7 This fictitious Dorset character died in Wiltshire. Who was she and
   how did she die?

8 Most of the inhabitants of this village were wiped out by the plague,
   but a stately home remains, one of the finest in the county.

9 A year or two after this famous Elizabethan built a castle, it was taken
   from him and he died in the Tower of London

10 A king was killed near Wimborne Minster, fighting the Danes. Who
    was he?

20 WRITERS

'Pentridge', oh my heart's
a-swelling
Full of joy with folk a-telling
Any news of this old place.

William Barnes

1 This contemporary editor and author writes books and articles on walks in Dorset.

2 This First World War soldier/poet had connections with Blandford Forum?

3 Shakespeare used the adventures of this Dorset man as the basis for *The Tempest.*

4 The 'Father of the English Sonnet' lies in Sherborne Abbey. Who is he?

5 The ancestors of this well-known poet can be traced to Dorset.

6 Who was the Dutch playwright who lived at Broadstone?

7 He was a rector who was also a naturalist. He wrote a book on the spiders of Dorset.

8 This grandfather of a Dorset poet and cleric lived at Woodyates and worked for fifty years with the Bank of England.

9 A writer who toured England in the early 1700s found Shaftesbury a 'sorry town' when he visited it. Who was he?

10 Name the novelist who lived at Skerryvore on Bournemouth's West Cliff from 1885-1887.

21 ROGUES AND ECCENTRICS

Yet must I die, and is there no relief,
So may my gracious King in mercy, save me.
Lines written by a highwayman
and poet to Charles I
(See question 7)

1 A notorious smuggler was married in Sixpenny Handley Church to the daughter of the landlord of the local inn. Who was he?

2 Who was the highwayman who stabled his horse in the village of Broadmayne while raiding coaches running between Weymouth and London?

3 Who was known as 'Captain of the Smuggling Band'?

4 This war-time traitor had an aunt living at Broadstone.

5 In an old rhyme, it was once claimed that this North Dorset town was famous for 'more rogues than honest man.' Which town?

6 In this remote spot where, in the eigthteenth century, deer-stealers abounded, smugglers hid their contraband.

7 A queen won a pardon for this young highwayman and poet. His family owned land in Dorset for 700 years, and there is a memorial to them at Church Knowle.

8 Who was the great dandy, son of a Weymouth apothecary, who paid £140,000 for the house he commissioned in 1717. It was largely demolished in1780 because its upkeep was too expensive.

9 Who built a house on the beach at Sandbanks?

10 Who was the eccentric seventeenth century squire who was said to have jumped his horse over a church.

22 GOD'S CREATURES

I call you, my brother...
If you hear me, come without fear.
The tide runs strongly. The water is cold
I am waiting and watching.
Come to me.
Celtic seal call.

1 Where will you find a horse with a red umbrella?

2 A stag and a lion feature in the surrounding parkland of this East Dorset estate. Which is the estate?

3 Where will you find red squirrels?

4 A creature of the wild spent a summer of the early 1960s in a Dorset Cove. What was it, and which was the cove?

5 Where can you see a skeleton of a bottle-nosed whale and a great bustard?

6 This little bird almost disappeared from the Dorset scene in the severe winter of 1962/3.

7 Where will you find a lion and a unicorn at the base of a large statue?

8 Sick and injured hounds, according to tradition, were sent here to recover when King John hunted wild boar in the Blackmore Vale.

9 There is an animal to be seen on the front of this Blandford building which was once an inn. What is it?

10 The animal on top of the maypole on Sturminster Marshall Green is the village emblem. What is it?

23 CHURCHES

An' parish churches in a string
Wi' tow'rs o' merry bells to ring.
William Barnes

1 The north aisle of this mainly fifteenth century church is believed to have come from the demolished cloisters of a nearby abbey church.

2 Name the Purbeck church believed to have been founded by St Aldhelm in AD 698.

3 Which twelfth century South Dorset church, standing adjacent to a manor house, has a rare bell tower?

4 There is no village near this church. It stands in a field but is clearly visible from the road between Dorchester and Sherborne.

5 Which church, now vested in the Redundant Churches Fund, has twin pulpits at the crossing and box pews?

6 This tiny church with a squat wooden tower stands in a farmyard.

7 Until about fifteen years ago this church had an unusual sound system. You could hear a recording of bells, the *Hallellujah Chorus*, or a short sermon from the vicar, by putting a few pence into a slot.

8 Which Dorset village church has a barrel organ which has recently been restored?

9 Which North Dorset town originally had twelve churches of which only four now remain?

10 It is one of the smallest churches in England. And it is also said to be the only one dedicated to St Edwold. Where is it?

24 MISCELLANEOUS

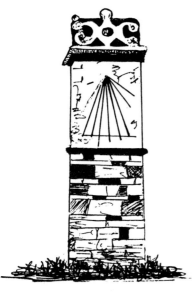

In Caundle, vor a day at least,
You woudden vind a scowlen feace,
Or dumpy heart in all the pleace.
William Barnes - See Question 7

1 Whose heart is said to have been eaten by a cat?

2 This ancient amphitheatre was the scene of savage gladiatorial fights and probably of martyrdoms in the days of the Romans.

3 In this house in a north Dorset village was held one of the courts of the infamous Judge Jeffreys during the Assizes following Monmouth's Rebellion.

4 Where is the Doll's House?

5 This building in Lyme Regis sounds as if it might be the right place to make for on a rainy day.

6 Most people have heard of Badbury Rings, but where and what are Buzbury Rings?

7 William Barnes wrote a poem after the victory at Waterloo. Which village did he name it after?

8 This village once had the tallest maypole in Dorset.

9 What is Shroton's other name?

10 Who did Cromwell call 'poor silly creatures'?

25 BATTLES

Sleep after toil, port after stormy seas
Ease after war, death after life, does greatly please.

Edmund Spenser. *The Fairie Queene 1 ix*

1 During World War II, an island was bombed by the Germans instead of a nearby town which was their target. Which was the island and which was the town?

2 This 2,000 strong band of protesters was routed at Hambledon Hill by Cromwell in 1645 during the Civil War. Who were they?

3 This 54-acre site, consisting of Iron Age ramparts, has yielded evidence of fierce fighting when the Romans attacked the hill fort.

4 Badbury Rings is still linked with a battle *c* AD 500 between a legendary hero king and invading forces. Who were the contestants.

5 Name the tenth century king who was killed in battle in East Anglia. His brother, to whom a church is dedicated, retired to Dorset and lived the life of a hermit at Cerne.

6 In the church at Minterne Magna is a memorial to this commander at Trafalgar.

7 Which Dorset hill fort was stormed in *c* AD 43 by the Second Roman Legion under Vespasian?

8 This castle was defended for the king during the Civil War, but it was shattered by Parliamentary forces and remains a ruin to this day.

9 A British general trained his troops in this village north of Blandford in preparation for a battle on the North American continent.

10 A defeated king of England waited here after a battle for a boat to take him to France.

26 RAILWAYS

These railroads ... they give us wings; they annihilate the toil and dust of pilgrimage.
Nathaniel Hawthorne

1 A collie dog called Rover died on the railway line at Creekmoor, Poole, in 1903. Where is his grave?

2 This railway, made redundant in the 1960s, stretched from Creekmoor to Broadstone. What now takes its place?

3 In what year did the Portland railway open?

4 The opening ceremony of this park was performed, by force of circumstances, on a railway station.

5 The arrival of the railway at this town in 1870 increased its population to around 17,000.

6 Though this town has undergone considerable development in recent years, its railway station has shrunk in size. Which town?

7 The name of this harbour was changed in 1884 as a result of the extension of the Great Western Railway.

8 Dorset's first railway once ran across part of this moor.

9 This steam train, built in 1925, ran from Paddington to the Welsh Valleys, and ended up in a scrapyard. Where is it now?

10 A railway embankment lies on one side of this mid-Dorset village and a river on the other. Near the railway line are the remains of an ancient castle.

27 COATS OF ARMS

Argent, three lions passant guardant in pale and in base a fleur-de-lis all gules. Above the shield is placed a gold mural crown with towers.

Blazoning of the coat of arms of Dorset County Council

1 The Bankes' family coat of arms can be seen on this manor house at Wimborne. Name the house.

2 What is unusual about the painted royal arms in Wyke Church?

3 There are six coats of arms displayed at this famous North Dorset public school, two of which are those of the Bishop of Salisbury, and two of the Horsey's of Clifton Maybank.

4 The royal arms of the reign of Queen Anne have been altered to those of George I in this village church in Blackmore Vale.

5 The arms of which ancient Dorset family are in the south window of the Horsey Chapel in St Andrew's Church, Melcombe Horsey.

6 There are now three coats of arms under the tower of St Peter's, Dorchester. Two came from other churches in the town. Where did the third come from?

7 Where did the shield in the front of the gallery in St Mary's Church, Puddletown come from and whose arms are on it?

8 The upper part of the Royal Arms painted over the chancel arch of St Gregory Church, Marnhull, has been cut off. How did this happen?

9 The arms of Queen Victoria are above the door of this south-west Dorset church and her jubilee is commemorated on panelling on its walls.

10 Royal arms are to be seen above the main entrance to St Nicholas Church, Moreton. Who were the royals believed to have worshipped here on visits to Weymouth?

28 MILLS AND WATERMILLS

He that wyll have any-
thinge done,
Let him com fryndly he
shall be welcom.
Part of an inscription of
1556 on the wall of
Fiddleford Mill House.

1 This mill, situated just below the castle at Corfe, has recently been bought by the National Trust. What is its name?

2 There is a trout stream in front of this picturesque watermill on the Dorset/Hampshire border. It is?

3 Name the eighteenth century mill at Cowgrove, Wimborne, which has recently been restored.

4 This mill stands on the banks of the river Stour south of Wimborne.

5 During the Second World War this mill and millhouse became the headquarters of the Fifteenth Platoon of Poole Home Guard

6 At which Dorset mill are nets made for fishing fleets all over the world?

7 This working watermill has an iron waterwheel, installed in the late nineteenth century to work a circular saw.

8 There were a number of fulling mills in Sherborne in the mid fifteenth century. What did they manufacture?

9 According to the *Domesday Book*, how many mills existed in Dorset when that survey was made in 1086?

10 There is a mill pond and a mill house dating from 1734 off the High Street of this town on the Dorset coast.

EAST DORSET
PICTURE QUIZ

1 In which churchyard is this unusual pyramid grave to be found?

2 This duckpond is a feature of a village in north Dorset. Which one?

3 Where and what is this buttressed building?

4 To what building in south-east Dorset is this castellated building the gatehouse?

5 Where is the cottage pictured below and who was the famous soldier/writer whose home it was?

6 What is the object pictured above and in what building will you find it?

7 This interesting stone building is in a remote mid-Dorset village. Which one? And for what purpose was it used?

8 Where and what is this house?

9 In which south Dorset village will you see this pump?

10 This part-Elizabethan manor house lies south east of Cranborne. What is its name?

WEST DORSET
PICTURE QUIZ

1 On the end of this terrace of houses, facing the church, is a Biblical text. In which village is it?

2 Where will you find this old anchor?

3 And this one?

4 Where will you find this exceptionally tall font cover?

5 This reed fringed and netted stretch of water has a purpose. What is this, and where is it?

6 These elaborate examples of floral art can be seen at an annual ceremony in Dorset. What is it – and where?

7 This unusual building attracts sightseers from near and far. What is it and where is it?

8 This church is situated about two miles east of the Somerset/Dorset border. It was rebuilt in 1879.

9 These stones are of great historical and archeological interest. What do they form part of and where will you find them?

10 The son of a well known historical character was baptised on November 1 1593 in this church, west of Long Burton. Who was he, and what is the church?

ANSWERS

1 DORSET BOOK OF RECORDS

1 Bulbarrow, at 902 feet.
2 In the museum at Shaftesbury. The date is 1744.
3 At Worldwide Butterflies and Lullingstone Silk Farm, Compton House, near Sherborne, where you can inspect piles of cocoons and silk moths.
4 Christchurch Priory. It was built nearly 900 years ago and is said to be the largest parish church in England.
5 The little-known village of Bourton, situated on the border near the Three Shires Stone, where Dorset, Somerset and Wiltshire meet.
6 The Chesil Beach. Its crest is 23ft above high water at Abbotsbury, and 43ft above high water at Portland.
7 The octagonal pillarbox at Barnes Cross, Holwell. It bears the VR cipher of Queen Victoria.
8 Poole Harbour, nearly 100 miles in circumference, if all its creeks and inlets are taken into account. Sydney Harbour, Australia, has always been considered to be the largest.
9 Ibberton It was one of six in Britain approved by the Countryside Commission.
10 Cranborne Chase, which once extended from Salisbury to Blandford, and was the resort of smugglers, bandits, and other vagabonds.

2 FAMOUS MEN

1 The Cerne Abbas Giant.
2 Dorchester's own hangman. He lived in the thatched cottage which still stands on the banks of the Frome not far from the prison.
3 Lawrence of Arabia. An effigy of him, in the flowing robes of a Bedouin Arab, is on his tomb there.
4 Thomas Dumberfield, who died in 1616 and William Dumberfield who died in 1646.
5 In Dorchester Museum.
6 Sir George Somers. He died in Bermuda, and his heart was buried there, although his body was brought back to Dorset.
7 General Robert Baden-Powell, who in 1907 launched the Boy Scout Movement on Brownsea Island in Poole Harbour.
8 Stuart Hibberd. He was the newsreader who made the announcement when King George V was dying; 'The King's life is moving swiftly to a close'.
9 Sir Winston Churchill. The incident occurred on the rustic bridge over Dean Chine at Branksome Park, Poole.
10 Thomas Hardy, the novelist, and Thomas Masterman Hardy, Nelson's Flag Captain at Trafalgar. Their common ancestor was also named Thomas Hardy.

3 THE ARTS

1 In the museum at Dorchester.
2 Henry Lee. He named it the New Theatre (Drury Lane) Bridport.
3 Olive Philpott.
4 John William Upham. He died in 1828 at Wyke Regis.
5 J M W Turner.
6 Alfred George Stevens. He accepted many commissions and designed the Wellington Memorial in St Paul's Cathedral, but died before it was set up.
7 The renowned English sculptor, Sir Francis Legatt Chantrey.
8 Edgar A Lane. On the 21 June 1897, as part of Queen Victoria's Diamond Jubilee celebrations, he conducted massed choirs in Maumbury Rings, Dorchester.
9 It was called the New Theatre and opened by James Shatford, the 40 year old son of a Gloucester doctor.
10 John Love. In 1790 he collaborated with James Fittler, the court engraver, to publish a series of twelve prints entitled, *Love's Picturesque views of Waymouth.*

4 CASTLES

1 Woodsford Castle. Inside are Norman rooms and a hall with a huge fireplace.
2 Shaftesbury.
3 Lulworth Castle, built of stone from Bindon Abbey. It was gutted by fire in 1929, after which it was partially rebuilt.
4 Sandsfoot Castle, built by Henry VIII in 1539.
5 Sir Walter Raleigh when he abandoned the idea of living in the old castle. The wings and towers were added by Sir John Digby.
6 Chideock Castle. It was taken and re-taken in the Civil War and was finally demolished by order of Parliament.
7 Pennsylvania Castle, Portland. John Penn, who was the Governor of Portland, was the grandson of William Penn, founder of Pennsylvania.
8 Portland Castle. It was built on the site of a Saxon castle.
9 Crawford Castle It is roughly circular, with one opening in the north-west. It was taken by the Roman Emperor, Vespasian, in AD 44.
10 Near to the Globe at Swanage. It was built for use as a restaurant.

5 SOME NOTABLE WOMEN

1 She was the prime mover in the building of the Herbert Home Hospital.
2 Margaret Beaufort. The tomb is in Wimborne Minster. The grammar school was dissolved by Edward VI, but set up again by Elizabeth I.
3 St Wolfride or Wolfrida.
4 *Tess of the D'Urbervilles.*
5 The Lady of Lyndlinch. She gave tithes from farms at West Parley and Woodlands to the rector of Lyndlinch, in which churchyard she is buried.
6 Mrs Bonham-Christie of Brownsea Island. During her ownership, notices warned off would-be visitors, and an armed keeper patrolled the shores.
7 Old Harry's wife! The chalk rocks rise from the sea off Ballard Down between Studland and Swanage
8 Miss Helen Brotherton. She established the Portland Bird Observatory in a disused lighthouse at Portland Bill and was connected with the public appeal for funds to endow Brownsea Island as a National Trust property and bird sanctuary.
9 Mrs Mary M Moule (neé Evans). She was wife of the vicar of Fordington, the Reverend Henry Moule, who was the incumbent there for fifty-one years.
10 Mrs Louise Dingwall. She trained her racehorses on the sand.

6 DORSET DIALECT

1 It is digging in search of food.
2 Earwigs.
3 'He can't see as well as he could'.
4 Shrew mouse.
5 'Might rain, you know.'
6 It is difficult.
7 Its wheels are stuck fast in soft soil.
8 Buttercups.
9 A stupid person.
10 This afternoon.

7 MEN OF THE CLOTH

1 The Reverend John Richards, alias Clavell. He built the folly known as Clavell Tower on the hill at Kimmeridge.
2 William Wake, born in 1657. He was the last Archbishop of Canterbury to travel by water from Lambeth Palace to the Houses of Parliament.
3 Dr Winnington Ingram. He also played squash and tennis.
4 The Reverend Henry Moule, who was at Fordington from 1829 to 1880. During the cholera epidemic, he invented a sanitation system which was widely adopted throughout the country.
5 Thomas Merke, whose life was spared after being sent to the Tower for treason.
6 St Mary, Charlton Marshall. He also built the old rectory at Spetisbury, now John's House. Both of these livings he held in plurality.
7 The Reverend John Pitt, ancestor of the two William Pitts
8 Tarrant Crawford. He was born and died there.
9 Samuel Wesley. He had nineteen children, and became rector of Epworth in Lincolnshire where he remained for forty years.
10 Aldrich Swan, vicar of Kington Magna.

8 MISCELLANEOUS

1 Charborough Tower in Charborough Park, erected by Thomas Erle-Drax. Hardy refers to it in *Two on a Tower*.
2 General Pitt-Rivers. He has been described as 'the father of English archaeology'
3 In Wimborne Minster. The dial of this astronomical clock – an amazing piece of machinery which has been restored in recent years – dates from the fifteenth or sixteenth century.
4 Hanging on the wall in the Priest's House Museum in Wimborne.
5 Bournemouth, or Sandbourne as Hardy refers to in *Tess of the D'Urbevilles*..
6 In the grounds of St Giles House, the seat of the Earls of Shaftesbury, at Wimborne St Giles. It was made by an Italian who would not allow anyone to watch him at work.
7 On Studland Heath – although it also grows in the Pyrenees.
8 Lord Antrim, Chairman of the National Trust, who promoted Enterprise Neptune – launched in 1965 to preserve the Dorset coastline.
9 Beaminster. It figures in *Tess of the D'Urbervilles*, Angel Clare's father being vicar there.
10 Twynham (Christchurch). The ducking-stool was said to be used to control chattering women.

9 INDUSTRY

1 At Lullingstone Silk Farm and Worldwide Butterflies, in the Old Manor at Over Compton, near Sherborne.
2 By discovering and using the now world-famous Portland stone, with which he built the Banqueting Room at Whitehall, London.
3 Colonel Waugh (William Petrie). He bought Brownsea Island in 1852, but finding the china clay was not the best in England, got into debt and escaped abroad.
4 Bridport. To be 'stabbed with a Bridport dagger' meant to be hanged with a Bridport rope.
5 The Bastard Brothers. After the disastrous fire of 1731, they were mainly responsible for the rebuilding of the town in Georgian style.
6 Gillingham. The factory is just off the Square.
7 Also at Gillingham in the 1930s. The workshops of Mr G B Gush and his partner, Mr Le Croisette, occupied the premises now used by the gloving factory.
8 John Mowlem He went up to London with only a few pennies in his pocket.
9 At Horton. The land was purchased in 1984 and has now expanded to eleven acres.
10 Sherborne. At this time it was Dorset's most populated town.

10 A QUESTION OF SPORT

1 At Southbourne, Bournemouth.
2 He was a famous sporting figure, and housed most of his hunt servants there.
3 A boat race. Toy boats are raced on the small stream.
4 Nurdling.
5 George Turberville, a scholar of Winchester College. He went as secretary to Thomas Randolph who was sent as ambassador to the Empress of Russia.
6 At the Bridport-Gundry Mill, Bridport.
7 George Chafin of Chettle House, Chettle.
8 At Badbury Rings by the Iron-age hillfort.
9 A real tennis court. It was designed by Mr F Cooper, a Dorset architect, and built in 1885 from local stone by Mr Gundry's grand-father, also Joseph Gundry.
10 Gigs, manned by a crew of six, would race each other out to ships in the bay, 'huffin' for business – that is, offering to guide ships in, in return for money.

11 CUSTOMS AND TRADITIONS

1 Woodbury Hill Fair Day which took place at Woodbury Hill, near Bere Regis.

2 A celebration at Sherborne, originating, it is said, from 1490 when the masons' work on the abbey was finally completed and they 'packed up'.

3 A festival in which Shaftesbury acknowledged its debt to the Lord of the Manor of Mitcombe for his help in a time of water shortage. The Bezant was a frame about four foot high, to which was fastened a trophy consisting of feathers, flowers, ribbons, jewels and trinkets.

4 Garland Day, when children of the fishermen's families made garlands of 'handsome flowers' which were taken out to sea and thrown onto the waves.

5 The Beating (or Perambulation) of the Bounds of the parish three days before, or on Ascension Day.

6 To allow the village to hold an annual fair within five days of St Martin's Day. The event, now revived, was originally a horse-market and amusement fair.

7 (a) A bonfire would be lit and everyone would follow a man with a child in arms around the fire, over which they would all leap, singing the jingle given at the top of page 15.
(b) The buying and selling of land by means of 'Church Gift', the parties going to church to make a declaration.

8 The Ooser, with its bull-like mask, probably representing a pagan god. By the nineteenth century it had become a Christmas Bull, roaming the streets and demanding refreshment from the villagers. Only Melbury Osmond's Ooser survived into the present century.

9 Public houses would be visited by the Purbeck Marblers in strange attire. They included ale-tasters, bread-weighers, and cannisters, and because of the town's history of fire, Surveyors and Searchers of Mantles and Chimneys who checked for obstructions in flues.

10 The Great Dorset Steam fair held at Tarrant Hinton.

12 TOWNS

1 Shaftesbury. The event is recorded in *The Woodlanders*.

2 Stalbridge, seven miles east of Sherborne It was once known as Staplebridge. Its 30ft high market cross dates from the early fourteenth century and is considered one of the finest in the county.

3 Shaftesbury again. It stands 700ft above sea level, and is the only hill town in the county.

4 Swanage. The tower was taken from the south side of London Bridge.

5   Swanage, again. Hardy referred to it as 'lying snug within two headlands as between a finger and a thumb'.
6   Dorchester. Until the 1960s Hardyes School occupied the site of the Hardye Arcade. It had been in South Street for more than 350 years.
7   Blandford Forum. It had a history of fires – in 1569, in 1676, in 1713 and in 1731 when it was almost completely burnt down. Even the fire engines were burned. The town was rebuilt by Act of Parliament and public subscription, and today is completely Georgian in the centre.
8   Gillingham in the Blackmore Vale, the most northerly town in Dorset. It appears in the *Domesday Book* as Gelingeham. It had a fine forest in the time of King John, who had a shooting lodge there.
9   Bournemouth.
10 Christchurch. The name 'Twinham' meant 'the place between the waters'. In 1539 it was described as 'set in a desolate place and slenderly inhabited'.

13 VILLAGES

1   Shapwick, lying close to the River Stour.
2   Batcombe.
3   Tolpuddle, in memory of the Tolpuddle Martyrs.
4   Ibberton on the lower slopes of Bulbarrow.
5   Holt, near Wimborne.
6   From the Conquest to 1500 its squires were the Mohuns, and the village was their 'ham', or home.
7   Gussage All Saints, Gussage St Michael, and Gussage St Andrew, known collectively as The Gussages.
8   Pentridge. The name comes from the Welsh, *pen* – a hill, and *Twrch* – a boar. Its church is dedicated to St Rumbold.
9   Chettle. A tablet in the tiny church records his death and that of his wife.
10 Shroton, sometimes known as Iwerne Courtney. The prisoners were known as Clubmen, a body professing to be neutral.

14 FOLKLORE

1   In Christchurch Priory. It was accidentally cut short during building operations, but during the night it was lengthened and placed in position without human aid.
2   On Bincombe 'Bumps' with its barrows and mounds which were settlements during the Stone and Bronze Ages. They are said to belong to the fairy-folk.

3 St Augustine is reputed to have struck his staff on the ground, whereupon the spring appeared.

4 A pet ape. It reputedly roams the house.

5 A Druid Temple. They are known as the Sarsen Stones.

6 The Winterborne. The river begins at Winterborne Abbas, and the story is told of a man who kept watch one evening, waiting for the river to rise. Half-frozen, he went home for a hot drink. Though only gone a few minutes, when he returned he found the river had risen.

7 Folke Church in the small, isolated village of Folke which lies midway between Long Burton and Alweston.

8 White Mill Bridge, Sturminster Marshall. The bell from the ruined church of Knowlton was said to have been stolen and dropped from the bridge by the thieves when pursued.

9 Because of the blasphemy of the crew. The bells are said to still toll from the sea-bed in storms.

10 St Aldhelm's Chapel on St Aldhelm's Head in the Purbecks. It dates from Norman times and during the 1200s was served by a Royal Chaplain.

15 DES RES

1 Cranborne Manor. Many royal and noble visitors stayed here for the hunting.

2 Poxwell Manor, south-east of Dorchester It has an attractive little gatehouse dating from 1634.

3 Athelhampton at Puddletown, near Dorchester.

4 Kingston Russell House, lying south-east of Long Bredy. It has a Palladian Portland stone front and four Ionic pilasters.

5 Herringston House standing in parkland at Winterborne Herringston.

6 Canford - the public school. John of Gaunt never came to it, although among its visitors were the Black Prince and Margaret Beaufort.

7 Thomas Gerard of Trent wrote these words about Mappowder Court, Mappowder in the *Survey of Dorset*, published in 1732.

8 Melbury Sampford. It was described by Horace Walpole as 'a sumptuous old seat in a fine situation'

9 Bingham's Melcombe in the village of Melcombe Bingham. Until 1895, it had been owned by the Bingham family for more than 600 years.

10 Crichel House, Moor Crichel. Humphrey Sturt of Horton inherited it in 1765.

16 PUBS

1 He called it The Horse on Hintock Green.
2 At the crossroads about four miles from Wimborne. It is the Horton Inn, a former posting house where coaches from London to Exeter changed horses.
3 The George Inn at Reforne, Portland, named after George III.
4 The George Inn at Reforne, Portland, again. The ship foundered on rocks off Portland.
5 At the western end of the village of Almer, near Charborough Park.
6 At Worth Matravers in the Purbecks.
7 The Bentinck Arms, situated at No 1 Maryland Cottage on Brownsea Island, and named after the George Augustus Cavendish-Bentinck, MP. It closed in the 1890s.
8 The Ship Inn on the Ridgeway at Upwey.
9 The Crown Hotel, Marnhull. Hardy called the village Marlott.
10 On the red brick inn at Tarrant Keynston.

17 MISCELLANEOUS

1 At Christchurch. It was opened in 1985, and has its entrance in the Priory car park.
2 At Poole. It was once the Guildhall, and is open to the public all the year round.
3 The well-known Constitution Hill at Parkstone, Poole.
4 St. Pancras in the village of Alton Pancras, the saint being a young nobleman who became converted to Christianity. At the age of fourteen he was taken before the Emperor Diocletian in Rome and ordered to renounce his faith or be thrown to the lions. Refusing to do so, he was slain with the sword.
5 On the plinth of the bronze statue of Barnes by Roscoe Mullins. It stands at the foot of the tower of St Peter's Church, Dorchester.
6 *Under the Greenwood Tree.*
7 At Worbarrow in the Purbecks. It is a great cliff, more than 550ft high, and was once an old British camp.
8 It was used in the Manor Court at Portland to keep the quarrymen's accounts. An example of a Reeve Pole can be seen in Dorchester Museum. It is made of old Spanish mahogany, is eight and a half feet long and one and a half inches square, and covered with cuts and notches.
9 Ackling Dyke, the Roman road which runs from Badbury Rings to Old Sarum.
10 Over the entrance to Lawrence of Arabia's cottage near Bovington Camp.

18 ROYALTY

1 The bones of St Edward the Martyr. They had lain in the rough lead box for reputedly some 400 years.
2 Queen Victoria.
3 Poole.
4 Sherborne Abbey.
5 George IV, when Prince of Wales, sent his daughter, Princess Charlotte Augusta, to Moor Crichel House. She died aged twenty-one.
6 Upton House. It was occupied by Prince Carol of Roumania from 1961 to 1969.
7 King Ine. In 705 he founded Sherborne Abbey for St Aldhelm who became the first Bishop of Sherborne. The see was removed to Salisbury in 1075.
8 Henry III. It was renewed by subsequent monarchs.
9 It was erected to commemorate Queen Victoria's Diamond Jubilee.
10 Henry VIII's widow, Catherine Parr.

19 UNNATURAL DEATHS

1 The Old Woman of Kimmeridge. The head and jaw had been placed beside her feet in the grave. It was assumed that she was a chronic gossip, and thus treated would be unable to continue the practice after death.
2 He was frozen to death whilst returning from Weymouth in a blizzard.
3 Surprised by excisemen when attempting to run a cargo of tea and gold across the Stour, he stepped into a hole in the river bed and, weighed down by the loot in his pockets, was drowned.
4 During the Monmouth rebellion. They took opposite sides, William Harvey being killed in a fight at Bridport.
5 Lady Trenchard. She was seen by the judge when dining at Wolfeton House, Charminster. He left abruptly and even before reaching Dorchester, his carriage was overtaken by a messenger on horseback with the news of her death.
6 Knowlton Church, off the Cranborne to Wimborne Road.
7 Tess of the D'Urbervilles. She was hanged.
8 Mapperton.
9 Sir Walter Raleigh. He was executed in 1618.
10 King Ethelred - not the Unready but the brother of King Alfred - in 871 AD. He is supposed to be buried there.

20 WRITERS

1 Rodney Legg.
2 Rupert Brooke. He was at Blandford Camp with the Royal Naval Division in 1915.
3 Sir George Summers, who was a keen seafarer.
4 Sir Thomas Wyatt.
5 Robert Browning. His first known ancestor – his great-grandfather of the same name – lived at Woodyates, near Pentridge, and died in 1746.
6 Jan Fabricius. He lived at Caesar's Camp, a house on Broadstone Heights, and was one of Holland's most renowned authors.
7 Octavius Pickard-Cambridge. He was rector of Bloxworth and died in 1917 after a ministry of forty-nine years.
8 Thomas Barnes. He was a forebear of the more famous William Barnes, poet, schoolmaster and clergyman.
9 Daniel Defoe. Its churches, chapels and shrines had beeen swept away at the Dissolution of the Monasteries.
10 Robert Louis Stevenson. When he was there, he wrote *Kidnapped* and *The Strange Case of Dr Jekyll and Mr Hyde*.

21 ROGUES AND ECCENTRICS

1 Isaac Gulliver. His smuggling operations spread from Poole to Lyme Regis.
2 Bill Watch. He used a barn which is now a private house.
3 Thomas Kingsmill, a native of Goudhurst in Kent. He had been a husbandman before becoming involved in smuggling.
4 William Joyce. In the Second World War he broadcast Nazi propaganda to Britain from Germany and was known as Lord Haw-Haw. He was executed for treason.
5 Shaftesbury.
6 Cranborne Chase in the east of the county.
7 John Clavell, a nephew of Sir William Clavell, for whom Queen Henrietta Maria won a pardon.
8 Bubb Doddington. The house, designed by Sir John Vanbrugh in the style of Blenheim Palace, is at Tarrant Gunville. Only part of the north wing remains.
9 Captain Simpson, in 1882 at Sandbanks betweem Shore Road and Flaghead Chine. It was not, in fact, built on sand, but on a clay outcrop. The captain lived there for only five weeks and in 1890 the Corporation considered it to be dangerous and it was blown up, leaving a pile of enormous concrete blocks. It became known as 'Simpson's Folly'
10 Conjurer Minterne. He jumped his horse over Batcombe Church from a steep hillside, knocking off a pinnacle.

22 GOD'S CREATURES

1 In High West Street, Dorchester. It is a restaurant.
2 Charborough Park. The Stag Gate and the Lion Gate are familiar features on the A31 between Wimborne and Bere Regis.
3 On Brownsea Island in Poole Harbour.
4 Sammy the Seal, the cove being Chapman's Pool in the Purbecks.
5 In the Natural History Museum, Dorchester.
6 The rare Dartford Warbler.
7 At Weymouth, on the statue of George III.
8 A house formerly standing on the site of Purse Caundle Manor. It was said to be a royal dogs' hospital.
9 A greyhound
10 A water rat

23 CHURCHES

1 All Saints, Hilton, situated above Milton Abbey Church.
2 St Martin-on-the-Walls at Wareham.
3 St Ann's Church, Radipole, Weymouth. It has a triple Italianate bell-tower.
4 St Mary's, Holnest. It has in recent times been saved from becoming a ruin.
5 St George's, Portland, built in 1777 of Portland ashlar stone.
6 Winterborne Tomson. It was restored in 1932 by A R Powys, the money being obtained from the sale of Thomas Hardy's manuscripts.
7 Witchampton.
8 St Michael and All Angels, Steeple in the Purbecks. It remained in use in the church from 1858 to circa 1890, until dismantled in 1943 and incorporated into the pipe organ at St Peter's, Church Knowle. It was restored in 1990.
9 Shaftesbury. The four remaining are St Peter, Holy Trinity, St James, and St Rumbold, the latter sited at Cann, though almost within the town.
10 Stockwood church in West Dorset.

24 MISCELLANEOUS

1 Thomas Hardy's. The story goes that on his death his heart was removed for separate burial, placed in a saucer and, it was said, accidentally eaten by Hardy's cat.
2 Maumbury Rings. It was referred to by Hardy as the Cirque of the Gladiators.
3 A house at Poyntington, once the home of the Cheneys. It is now a farmhouse.
4 At West Lulworth. It is a tiny cottage originally built by an American as a holiday home.
5 The Umbrella Cottage with its umbrella-shaped thatched roof.
6 Above Langton, about two miles south of Blandford. They are the remains of an ancient hill fort.
7 Bishop's Caundle. It is a lengthy poem describing the celebrations which took place on the village green after the victory.
8 Shillingstone. It was 86ft high.
9 Iwerne Courtney.
10 The Dorset Clubmen who were routed by Cromwell during the Civil War.

25 BATTLES

1 Brownsea Island, off Poole. On the night of 24 May 1942, a strategic night decoy, consisting of a string of twenty oil drums filled with cordite, was fired with dramatic result.
2 The Dorset Clubmen, 2,000 farmers and yeoman, armed only with clubs, banded together to protest at the constant plundering of the opposing forces.
3 Hod Hill. The site is now owned by the National Trust.
4 King Arthur and the invading Saxons.
5 King Edmund of East Anglia, his brother being Edwold, to whom the church at Stockwood is dedicated.
6 Sir Henry Digby.
7 Maiden Castle, south-west of Dorchester.
8 The old castle at Sherborne, built by Roger, Bishop of Salisbury, between 1107 and 1135.
9 General Wolfe - in preparation for the storming of the Heights of Abraham.
10 Charles II waited at Charmouth after the Battle of Worcester, disguised as a groom in a runaway wedding party. He missed the boat - or rather, the boatman was missing - and continued on to Bridport, landing in Normandy forty-one days later.

26 RAILWAYS

1 At Upton Park, Poole, in a pets' cemetery which was discovered when the ground was being cleared of undergrowth.
2 Broadstone Way, part of the new road scheme.
3 On 16 October 1865. In 1900 the railway to Easton was completed.
4 Poole Park. A severe storm occurred on the eve of the opening ceremony in 1890, damaging the pavilion and much else besides. The park was eventually declared open by Edward VII from the booking office of Poole railway station.
5 Bournemouth.
6 Poole.
7 Bridport harbour. Its name was changed to 'West Bay' to distinguish it from the town and to suggest a holiday resort.
8 Hartland Moor, a National Nature Reserve. The railway was named Frayle's Tramway, after a London potter who built it in 1806 to transport clay from Norden to the edge of Poole Harbour.
9 It was rescued in 1976 and restored. It now carries visitors between Swanage and Norden, the track having been restored by the Swanage Railway Company.
10 Spetisbury. When excavations were made for the track of the Central Dorset Railway in 1857, a large grave was discovered containing the remins of fifty skeletons, one of which had a spear embedded in its skull.

27 COATS OF ARMS

1 Over the door of Kingston Lacy House, Wimborne.
2 It was origially the arms of George I. Later two more 'I's' were added to alter it to those of George III.
3 Sherborne School.
4 Ss Mary and James, Hazelbury Bryan.
5 The arms of the Turges who were Lords of Melcombe Horsey.
6 One came from All Saints', another from Holy Trinity, and the third from the old post office.
7 It is said to have been taken from a ship. On it are quartered the arms of England and France.
8 When the roof at the east end of the nave was partially lowered in the nineteenth century.
9 St Mary, Burton Bradstock.
10 Either Princess Charlotte, daughter of George III, or her uncle, the Duke of Gloucester, both frequent visitors to Moreton.

28 MILLS AND WATERMILLS

1 Boar mill.
2 Alderholt Mill. The trout stream is in front, and the big wheel to the rear.
3 White mill, dating from 1776.
4 Canford mill. It is near the manor house and church.
5 Creekmoor mill and millhouse.
6 At Bridport-Gundey mill, Bridport. They also make the nets used by the space shuttle.
7 Melbury Abbas mill. It has a millpond and is open throughout the year.
8 Cloth. The cloth was made more compact during manufacture – a process called 'fulling'.
9 A total of 280. Now only very few remain.
10 Off the High Street in Swanage.

29 EAST DORSET PICTURE QUIZ

1 Spetisbury. It is in memory of the Reverend Thomas Hackett, a former rector of the parish, and his wife, Dorothy.
2 Ashmore, Dorset's highest village.
3 At Tarrant Crawford. It formerly belonged to the monastic buildings, but is now a modern cow parlour.
4 Bindon Abbey in the Purbecks.
5 Cloud's Hill, T E Lawrence's cottage at Bovington, now National Trust property and frequently open to the public.
6 A fire bucket. It hangs in Puddletown Church.
7 Woolland in the Blackmore Vale. It is now privately owned, but was once the schoolhouse.
8 Woolbridge Manor at Wool, seen from the rear.
9 Osmington.
10 Edmondsham House. The rounded gables of the wings create a Dutch effect.

30 WEST DORSET PICTURE QUIZ

1 Frampton. The text is 'Yea they may forget yet will I not forget thee'.
2 Outside the Anchor Pub at Seatown. It belonged to the *Hope* of Amsterdam which ran aground in January 1748, and was 'caught' by a fisherman in 1985.
3 Outside the Avalanche Church at Portland. It was bought up from the bed of the ocean when the wreck of the *Avalanche* was discovered in 1954.

4 In Cattistock church, in the chapel beneath the tower. It is 20ft high.
5 It is the Duck Decoy in the Swannery at Abbotsbury.
6 The well-dressing at the Wishing Well, Upwey, Weymouth which takes place annually in the first week in May.
7 The Umbrella Cottage at Lyme Regis.
8 St Michael, Beer Hackett.
9 They form part of the old Roman wall at Dorchester.
10 Walter, the second son of Sir Walter Raleigh. A copy of the entry from the Bishop's Transcripts hangs on the south wall of St Martin, Lillington.

Front cover: The Globe, at Durlston Park, Swanage. It weighs 40 tons and was set up by George Burt in 1887.
Back cover: At Barnes Cross, near Holwell. It was made by John M Butt & Co of Gloucester between 1853 and 1856.
Title page: Briantspuddle, one of the seven villages in the Puddle or Piddle Valley.

KEY TO LINE DRAWINGS OF SPECIFIC SUBJECTS

BIBLIOGRAPHY

Dorset Dialect Days by James Attwell
Dorset by Michael Pitt Rivers
Dorset Today and Yesterday by F S Hinchy
Hardy's Rivers by Monica Hutchings. Harmondsworth Penguin 1986.
The Hardy Guides by Hermann Lee
The King's England - Dorset by Arthur Mee. Hodder and Stoughton, revised 1967.
The Dorset Year Book
Dorset Life magazine.

ACKNOWLEDGEMENTS

My thanks to Eric Ricketts, FRIBA and to the staff of Dorset County Library and Dorset Museum for their assistance.